High-Frequency READERS

LUNCH

Written by Gay Su Pinnell
Illustrated by David Bamundo

Scholastic Inc.
New York Toronto London Auckland Sydney
Mexico City New Delhi Hong Kong

Copyright © 2000 by Scholastic Inc.
SCHOLASTIC, HIGH-FREQUENCY READERS, and associated logos and designs are
trademarks and/or registered trademarks of Scholastic Inc.
All rights reserved. Published by Scholastic Inc.
Printed in the U.S.A..
ISBN 0-439-06452-X

3 4 5 6 7 8 9 10   23   05 04 03 02 01 00 99

I like apples.

I like sandwiches.

I like bananas.

I like pizza.

I like cookies.

I like milk.

I like lunch.